THIS BOOK

BELONGS TO

_____

·WE·WISH·

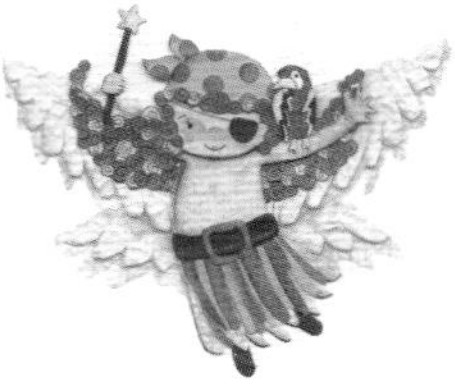

Published by University College Falmouth 2006

University College Falmouth
Woodlane, Falmouth
Cornwall TR11 4RH
www.falmouth.ac.uk

ISBN 0 9505680 2 3
ISBN 978 0 9505680 2 7

Book design by Peter Bennett, St Ives, Cornwall.
Printed and bound in Great Britain by R. Booth Ltd, Penryn, Cornwall.

HOPES AND DREAMS OF CORNWALL'S CHILDREN
FOREWORD BY THANDIE NEWTON

PUBLISHED BY UNIVERSITY COLLEGE FALMOUTH – ALL PROCEEDS TO THE NSPCC

University College
FALMOUTH

NSPCC
Cruelty to children must stop. FULL STOP.

Contents

It's easy to dismiss the atmosphere of our first years, but as the shadows of our past cross other shadows, people, cultures and experiences, we realise the uniqueness of where we began.

The vibrant folklore veined through every aspect of Cornish life touches everyone who makes it their home. It was seamlessly attached to all the places I'd visit as a child. I could practically hear the giant throw the rock that became St Michael's Mount, see the sky-large sea cat sweep its paw into the port at Mousehole, hear the call of the mermaid for the drowned boy as we drove through Zennor.

It's only now, considering *We Wish*, that I realise how fertile the culture of Cornwall is, and how easy it became for me to enrich every situation with layers of magic and meaning. A simple family walk would be a hike to Prussia Cove, running around empty mines at Tintagel, rolling down the sand dunes at Sennen, picking blackberries near the Merry Maidens, cycling along the seafront to get fresh fish from the Newlyn fishermen, or catching the low tide for a visit to the Mount, where my brother and I would run round the battlements, pretending we were defending the realm.

And for the family meal, Star Gazy Pie? Or a pasty from Philps in Hayle? As the pastry crumbs gathered on my chest, I used to wonder what it would be like to eat one as the miners did, with meat and veg in one end and sticky sweet pudding in the other. Or, on Good Friday in Helford, cockles which we'd pluck from the shallows and toss into bubbling pots on open fires dotted along the beach. Or how about fish and chips, drenched with malt vinegar, sparkling with salt, eaten in our car looking out over The Lizard?

The Lizard. Gurnard's Head. Mousehole. Lamorna Cove. With names like these, how can a person not be hypnotised?

The stony ground, which made the land unworkable, meant that Cornwall has retained the ancient glory of an unspoilt landscape. No wonder the finest theatre in the county is hewn out of a hillside, the open-air Minack. We'd sit on blankets, with crab sandwiches and tea, marvelling at this temple, the sound of the sea in our ears and stars winking all around. Another shrine to the arts, Tate St Ives, celebrates the age-old tradition of artists christened by Cornwall: Patrick Heron, Barbara Hepworth, Peter Lanyon, Alfred Wallis… What alchemy has inspired this rich artistic tradition?

Cornwall is the end of the road, and the port to the world: an end and a beginning. We feel rooted by what is ancient around us. There's a security, which allows for innocence, and a wisdom, which gives strength.

I was reminded of this when I read the poems written by these fantastic kids; the innocence and the knowing. From their corner of Cornwall, they embrace the events the world sends via the media and their education. But when they stand looking out at the sea from Prussia Cove, it must be hard to believe that this world is being so woefully harmed by its most sophisticated inhabitants. If the wagers of war could stand feeling the breeze, the grass underfoot, seeing the sun melt into the skyline, could they feel anything other than a desire to embrace humanity and our planet?

The young will change the world. The kids writing on these pages will take their wishes, their dreams for the future, and tread the path to a brighter tomorrow.

THANDIE NEWTON

As children's authors the welfare of children is close to our hearts, so when we were asked to judge a selection of writing by schoolchildren from all over Cornwall in support of the NSPCC, we were delighted to accept.

Judging the competition was a pleasure. The entries showed a wonderful wealth of imagination and talent: stories about fish that grant wishes, stepping into paintings and meeting mermaids; poems about fulfilling dreams such as becoming famous sports stars, having a pony or being an explorer. Amusing wishes for magic football boots and teachers who take you water-skiing made us smile, and heart-rending wishes for families to be whole again or for everyone to be accepted for themselves brought a lump to our throats.

Even more inspiring was the care for humanity that shone through the entries. Many children wrote about their longing for peace, their concern for the environment, their yearning for a better world where no one starves and there are no wars. Others wrote pieces directly relevant to the work of the NSPCC, imagining what life must be like for children suffering from cruelty or neglect. Proof that no matter how different children's lives are today, their basic needs are unchanging – a loving family and a safe, secure environment to grow up in. Proof that, no matter how hi-tech their lives with their computers, mobile phones and PlayStations, children still have a sense of justice and care what happens to other people and the world we all live in.

It was a difficult task to choose the prize-winners – there were so many we would like to have rewarded. We based our selection on talent, imagination and originality. Where there were two similar entries we went for the one with the stronger voice, the one that put the message across in the best way.

Reading these pieces will make you laugh, smile – and think. Our children are worried about the future of the world, hurt and bewildered by the needless suffering of other children, by the injustice and wars across the world, and often they feel powerless to do anything about it. We need to listen to their worries and realise the effect our decisions have on them. Every child should have the right to a safe, secure and loving home, food and clean water and a good education. We are pleased to have this opportunity to support the NSPCC in their work to make this wish come true.

Karen King AND June Crebbin

Illustration:
Eleanor Rudge

11

My family

Peter wants a mansion,
A pool and a PS2.
Fran wants a motorbike
To travel to Timbuktu.
Mum wants a garden,
With sprinklers and all the rest.
Dad wants a racing car,
But he hasn't passed his test.
I guess that's all the family –
Well, all except for me.
I want to keep my family
As close as close can be.

Jane Kurth

Illustration:
Hannah Cumming

Fish for tea

I wish I was Ronaldinho, flying down the wing,
Skipping past five players, making the crowd sing.

I wish I was a penguin, speeding through the sea,
Sliding on my tummy, eating fish for tea.

I wish I was a skier, flying in and out,
Got to beat the clock - hear the crowd shout!

I wish I was a snowy owl, flying through the sky,
I see a little mouse, I know it's going to die!

Harry McMellon

Illustration:
Katherine Child

There must be a way

Tegan Jack

his poem is not a happy one
With bunnies and rainbows and a big shiny sun.
This is the truth, which I'm afraid to say
Is happening around us, every day.

A girl and boy
Lay on the street,
With no one to love
But the dog at their feet.

They'd lived with Auntie and Uncle
Since their Mum and Dad died.
But Uncle kept hitting them,
And Auntie just cried.

She lay on her bed
Night and day,
Until Uncle got arrested
And Auntie went away.

The children were left
To fight for themselves,
With nothing left
But dust on their shelves.

They wished for someone,
Someone to love.

Stories like this
Affect lives every day,
But we can stop this –
There must be a way.

Illustration:
Jennifer Way

Tea with the octopus

I wish I could swim with the dolphins,
That I could surf on the breaks of the sea,
That I could go to tea with the octopus.

I wish I could swing with the monkeys,
That I could roar like a lion or a tiger,
That I could break boulders like a rhino.

I wish I could slide like a snake on the sand,
That I could walk on the sand like a camel,
That I could sneak like a thorny devil.

Victoria Rose Naylor

Illustration:
Hannah Cumming

A basketball dream

Felix de Rijke Thomas

Zak loved basketball. He always wore his Gorrilaz basketball kit. Zak is dark-skinned,with black frizzy hair and thick braids stuck tight to his head like ivy to a pillar.

One day he was invited to a basketball match with his friends. Zak was so excited he ran down the street and burst through the door, where he found his Mum cutting a chicken for dinner.

"Saturday?" said his Mum. "Oh, I'm sorry – we've been invited to your uncle and aunt's house."

"But, but..." His eyes filled with tears. "It's Gorillaz against the Knights!" It was all too much for Zak and he stormed upstairs to his room.

When it was dark, he lay awake on his bed. "What I really want is to be a professional basketball player and play for the Gorrilaz," he thought. "But that will never happen."

When the dreaded day came, Zak sulked in the car all the way to his aunt's and uncle's house.

"Hello Aunt," he said, then slipped away. Gingerly, he stepped through a door and saw that the room was filled with shiny basketball trophies.

"Uncle, did you win all these trophies?"

"Yes, I did."

"Please could you teach me some moves?" asked Zak.

"Yes, I'll try"

His uncle made him work hard. After months of practice Zak was good enough for a trial to play for the Gorrilaz. And the coach was impressed.

"You're in!" he said.

Later on, Zak stepped onto the court. It was like a dream. The stadium was chock-full, the crowd was booming and roaring like a stampede of bulls, the smell of victory was in the air.

The match began.

Illustration: John Aggs

Leave some fish in the seas!

I went swimming in the deep blue sea,
And saw what I did not expect to see:
There were no fish swimming with me.
I remember when I saw one hundred coloured fish,
And so this is my wish –
Why don't you listen to this?
Fishermen, please leave some fish in the seas!

Tom Medvedev

Illustration:
Robert Allwood

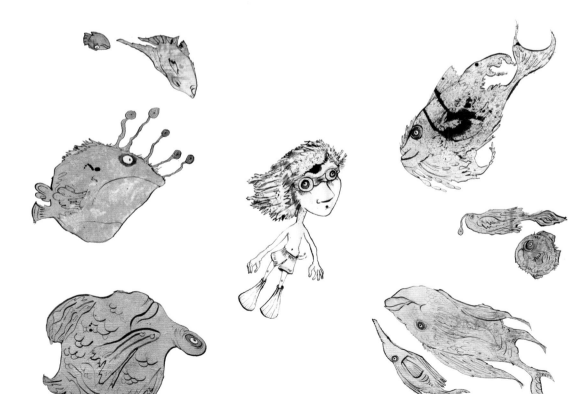

Squirrel and the Wish Fish

Squirrel was racing through the forest. His bushy tail got caught in some thorny brambles. Squirrel tripped over it and sighed, "I wish I had a different tail. I wish it was like a dog's or cat's tail."

He sat on the lake's edge. A strange bubbling sound came from beneath the murky water and a little fish poked his head out of the lake.

"Hello," glugged the fish. "I am your Wish Fish!"

Squirrel stared at the Wish Fish with confused eyes.

Wish Fish said again, "I am your Wish Fish and I can give you three wishes. Yes, I did say three! Please use them wisely or you may lose your hair! Now let's begin with your first wish…" Wish Fish nodded four times. Each time he nodded, Squirrel's tail grew longer and thinner!

Soon Squirrel's tail was too long and he had to drag it behind him! "Oh well!" sighed Squirrel, "I'll show Cat. She'll like it."

So Squirrel went off to Cat's tree. She took one look at Squirrel and started to giggle. Then she chuckled. And then she was laughing like mad! Squirrel slouched back to the lake, his head hung low. He decided to use his next wish to cheer himself up.

"I wish the whole forest was covered in acorns!" he yelled. Wish Fish clapped his fins together and an avalanche of acorns came flowing towards them. Soon, all of the forest was deeply covered in acorns!

Wish Fish and Squirrel poked their heads out of the acorns. "Oh no!" cried Squirrel. "I wish that everything was back to normal." Wish Fish winked, all the acorns vanished and Squirrel's tail turned bushy again.

He doesn't any more care if it gets in the way of everything. He likes it just the way it is.

Jasmine Molloy

Illustration:
Genna Byrne

18

Perfect school day

Tom Hills

The teacher stood and beamed at us –
"Come on you kids, grab your coats!
You're going to learn how to water-ski
Around a castle moat!"
I wish…

The teacher is speaking on the phone,
But no-one knows who to.
Until he turns to me and says:
"Sir Alex Ferguson needs you!"
I wish…

"For science today," said the teacher happily,
"I've made a chocolate mound.
You can eat all you like, children,
Until you're completely round!"
I wish…

Illustration:
Hannah Cumming

Into the painting

Emily Munoz

Illustration:
David Plant

I wish I was in that painting. The London Thames is frozen and everyone is having such fun on the ice." POP!

I was slowly lifted off the ground and found myself zooming towards the painting. I was going to crash! But I didn't – I went straight through its surface and glided gracefully to the ground. It was beautiful; everyone was skating and it appeared to be Christmas, because there were lights reflected on the frozen river. Everyone was having so much fun.

"I wish I could go on the ice, but I don't have any skates." POP!

In my hands lay a pair of sky-blue skates, silver around the edges with golden blades. I put them on and raced onto the ice, into the middle, performing a huge twirl. I was having so much fun, until I looked up and saw the sun shining onto the ice.

"Attention everyone! You have to get off the ice! The ice is melting!" shouted a man with a huge megaphone on the Millennium Bridge. I skated to the side and sat down on the edge, panting. "That was fun," I gasped. "What shall I do next?" My eyes drifted towards the London Eye and I smiled. "I wish I could be on the London Eye." POP!

I was there, and could see everything: Buckingham Palace, Big Ben, the Houses of Parliament – EVERY-THING! The glass compartment went round and round. Passing the camera, I held up the skates and smiled. When the ride was finished I collected the photograph and said, "I wish I could go home now." POP!

Scrutinising the painting later, I find that I'm right there in the centre, skating for all to see!

20

Kinder world

I wish there
was a kinder world
for people
everywhere.

Water would be clean and pure,
Illness and disease no more.
Swiftly all the children run through school gates,
Having a laugh with all their mates.

With open spaces for people to run –
It's amazing to see children have fun.
Some day soon I hope there'll be
More happy children just like me.

Jessica Toy

Illustration:
Fiona Gowan

Kids R Us

**ant to improve your child's life?
Want to give your child excitement?
Visit Kids R Us and check out our brand-new
inventions for kids!**

Here are some of our newest inventions at low, low prices…

Think Fruity Drops
Are your kids bored in class and not paying attention? Let them try some Think Fruity Drops, and watch their grades go sky-high! Not only do they experience the sweet fruitiness, they also pay attention in class for up to three hours each sweet!

School Jet 5000
Is you child always late for school because of sleeping in? The School Jet 5000 may look like an ordinary backpack, but inside there's a jetpack with rocket fuel that lasts up to twenty years and doesn't harm the environment!

Pen Watch
This new invention improves handwriting, from the most sluggish to the best in the class, within ten seconds of putting on the watch. Not only does this product improve your child's writing – it also has a tracking device for safety!

Smart-O-Matic
Now, with the Smart-O-Matic, not only does the teacher use the smartboard, but so do the children! This device is an interactive whiteboard, built into school desks. Using the Smart-O-Matic, paper is saved and so is the environment.

Olivia Dunlop

Illustration:
Eleanor Rudge

Sophie's secret

Marina Scott

an you keep a secret?
Because I've got
one I'm itching to tell!

It all started out when I heard about the poor whale that died in the Thames. Oh, by the way – I'm Sophie, Sophie Sushton, and I'm a HUGE fan of animals. In fact, I'm running a kids' campaign to help the environment, as millions of them die every year because of pollution.

About this whale... I was SO upset when it died that the moment Mum broke the news to me I lunged up the stairs and into my room, with all its posters of cats and other creatures. As soon as I got there I started to cry. Not like a little-girly cry – oh no! This one was silent, but it lasted just as long.

"How can people be so cruel?" I asked myself through my sobs. "I wish people would stop being cruel to animals!" I exclaimed angrily, hugging my cat Spottina tightly to my chest.

A bright light suddenly blinded me. When I opened my eyes the light was still there, but it was dimmer and now I could see where it was coming from. For a few moments I couldn't speak. The light was coming from... SPOTTINA! Then, suddenly, it went out!

What had happened? Who knows?
That's just what I'm puzzling about
at the moment.

Illustration:
Nick Mott

24

A wish that came true

Torin Arnold

I wish I could see the future,
I wish I could see the past,
I wish I could sing a rap,
I wish I could run like the wind,
I wish I could touch the stars,
I wish I could bounce on clouds,
I wish I could rest on the sun,
I wish I could write a poem.

Illustration:
Jasmine Foster

25

Don't just wish for yourself

Hetty Fruer-Denham

See you on Monday," I said, as the last of my friends left. It had been the best birthday party ever! Mum was clearing up, so I went upstairs to my room. There were party streamers and balloons everywhere. I grabbed one and it popped suddenly. And out came... a teddy bear! Just floating... floating in the air!

"I'm a fairy," it said.

"A fairy?"

The teddy fell to the ground, and behind it *was* a fairy!

"Yes," it called. "And the number of wishes I can give you is two. But remember – be careful what you wish for." I closed my eyes. I just couldn't believe what was happening.

"I wish... I wish I was a king!" I shouted. When I opened my eyes, I was in front of an enormous palace made of pure gold, glinting in the sunlight.

I had the biggest feast! With cheese, ham and chocolate-spread sandwiches, cakes and buns, hot chocolate and banana milkshakes – just for me!

"I'm full!" I said at last. "It's time for my next wish. I wish, I wish…" I looked around and saw that all this was stupid – I hated being king. "I wish there was world peace!"

The fairy suddenly appeared and sprinkled something over me. I closed my eyes. I was home.

"Because you wished something for everyone else and not just for you, you shall become a fairy too!" said the fairy. PUFF! I looked at myself and saw a beautiful fairy with coloured wings.

Now I travel the world making children's wishes come true. Maybe I'll come and visit you!

Illustration:
Lisa Zibamanzar Mofrad

Brother

Thomas Wills

I wish I had a brother,
A very sporty brother.
He'd be good at cricket,
I will never get a wicket.

I wish I had a brother,
A very good brother.
He'd be very nice,
And never get head lice.

I wish I had a brother,
A very wild brother.
He'd play the clown
When Mum's in town.

I wish I had a brother,
A very fast brother.
He'd whiz right past,
And I'd finish last.

I wish I had a brother,
I'll ask my mother.
I don't want any other,
I JUST WANT A BROTHER!

Illustration:
Tone Schmidt

If only wishes would come true

Isabel Evans

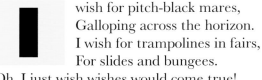

I wish for pitch-black mares,
Galloping across the horizon.
I wish for trampolines in fairs,
For slides and bungees.
Oh, I just wish wishes would come true!

I wish for everyone to be happy,
With smiles all around.
I wish for characters in books to come climbing out,
Harry Potter or Ratty.
Oh, I just wish wishes would come true!

I wish to see a dolphin jump across the sunset,
Beautiful, elegant and wet.
I wish to travel the world,
And to speak in many tongues.
Oh, I just wish wishes would come true!

I wish for many more wishes,
But I think that isn't allowed.
Oh I just wish wishes would come true,
But sadly, I know that they don't do!

Illustration:
Chris Burge

Time machine

I wish that I were an explorer finding strange lands and exotic creatures.
I wish that I could be invisible so that I could disappear
When my bedroom needed tidying!
I wish that I owned a zoo but all the animals were so tame
That people could go into the cages with them.
I wish I had my own island
Where everything was made out of sweets, even the animals.
I wish drawings could come to life so that anything you drew
Would come off the paper and stand right next to you!
I wish that I could visit far away countries,
Taking food and water to all who need it.
I wish I could fly on a shimmering dragonfly as it glides over a glistening lake.
I wish I had a miniature pet that could fit in my pocket
To keep me company when I'm lonely.
I wish I could read people's thoughts as they stare at me across the room.
I wish I could have a time machine and travel to the future
To see if any of my wishes come true!

Naomi Sandercock

Illustration:
Ellie Cryer

A polite girl

Rhiannon Iles

I wish I were a fairy that could glide up high...

"Rhiannon!" shouted my teacher from across the classroom. "Why aren't you working?"

"I'm sorry, Miss Mingle. I... I was just dreaming. Sorry."

Suddenly, without warning, I transformed into a tiny, beautiful fairy. I jumped down from my massive chair and sneakily crept out of the classroom without anyone noticing. In the large corridor I heard Miss Mingle ask Sophie if she knew where I'd disappeared to. She had no idea. (Sophie's my best mate – she sits right next to me.) Finally I had escaped from school!

I had all the freedom in the world, so I decided to go exploring. I found a small, pink, sparkly palace. It looked just my size, so – being a polite girl – I knocked on the door. No-one answered, so I walked in.

"Hello!" I called. "Is anyone in?" No-one replied, not a single soul.

I looked around the palace. It seemed posh, and there was a large box of those expensive Thornton's chocolates on a nearby table. Carefully lifting the lid, I took one. Yum, mocha cream-flavoured centre! Addictive! I ate another three and was full. I settled onto one of the brown leather sofas. Rather cold, but I'd get used to them.

Finally, I felt it was time to return home. But how would I transform back to my normal self? On my way back, I met a snail and he astounded me by offering to help, suggesting that I try hiding in a mulberry bush for five minutes. I did, and soon I was my normal self again!

I thanked the snail – being a polite girl – and ran off home. Opening the door I shouted hello to Mum as if it were any ordinary school day. I parked myself, as usual, on the sofa to watch a television programme – about mulberry bushes!

Illustration:
Clare Elsom

Whole and happy

I wish that my family were whole and my Mum and Dad didn't fight,
And my Dad would live with my Mum.
I wish I could live back in my old house on my old street.
I wish I was more confident at maths.
I wish I could speak up more and join in with more clubs and activities.
I wish my sisters got on with me more and wouldn't fight with my Mum.
I wish my Dad wouldn't smoke.
I wish I could play the drums.
I wish the world wouldn't fight and have wars,
But be happy and nice to each other.

RP

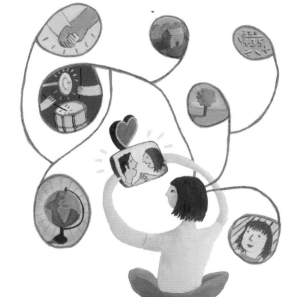

Illustration:
David Bain

No, not now

Shannon Mannix

I wish, I wish,
I wish upon a star,
That I could have all the toys, near and far.
No! Not now, I want something better,
I want a brand new glittery sweater.

I wish, I wish,
I wish upon a fairy,
I want a dolly whose name is Mary.
No! Not now, I want something girly,
I want something pink, not to mention twirly.

I wish, I wish,
I wish upon a pond,
That I could be just like James Bond.
No! Not now, I want something funky,
I want a brand new purple monkey.

I wish, I wish,
I wish upon a book,
That I could have the perfect look.
No! Not now, I want something puffy,
I want a kitten all cute and fluffy.

I wish, I wish
I wish upon a mother,
That I could have a new sister or brother.
No! Not now, I want something done,
I want world peace for everyone!

Illustration:
Lisa Zibamanzar Mofrad

In my future

Madeleine Grace Freight

I want to see blue sky and breathe in fresh air,
I want flowers and trees in every town and village square.
I want to hear the birds chirp and sing,
And hear every church bell ring
For the freedom of the people everywhere.
I want to hear laughter and joy.
From now to ever after,
This is my future.

In my future
I do not want pain and disaster.
All people should be freed from stress.
No more violence or starvation,
But love and peace in every nation.
No more homelessness – it causes such loneliness.
From here to ever after,
This is my future world.

Illustration:
Amy Hearn

33

Football crazy

Tom Coles

I wish I could be a professional footballer, but my Mum and Dad say you have to train really hard and have to be picked.

But there are other things I wish I could be or do. I'd like to be an artist or an architect, and I'd like to run the Olympics. I wish I could have a motorbike, and be really strong.

I wish I could do all these things. But if I can't I'll carry on being as brilliant as I can in goal, and riding anything like bikes, skateboards and rollerblades. The thing I mostly wish to be is a professional footballer, because I like my football and I play as much as I can for my two teams – Southgate Colts and my school Altarnun.

The thing is, though, I haven't been spotted by a scout. I really wish I could be spotted, because when I get older I would have a chance of playing for Plymouth Argyle. I could be spotted by premiership clubs and go on to be a professional goalkeeper. That would be my wish come true, and I would be the happiest person alive.

Illustration:
Kine Solberg

Rainforests

Will anyone save those rainforests,
And all the animals there?
Please someone stop the logging –
It seems like no one really cares!
Soon all the animals will be dying,
But the farmers want more.
I want the exact opposite,
That's what I wish for.
Logging doesn't just kill the animals,
It harms us as well.
Think of all the medicines,
Without them it would be hell.
What about oxygen –
That's something the loggers forgot!
You probably will know
We need oxygen a lot.
I hope someone stops pollution,
Which is partly to blame
For water tasting horrible,
Years ago it wasn't the same.
The sky is a different colour,
It's a dark and dirty grey.
Something is not right,
It's getting worse day by day.

Matthew Horwell

Illustration:
Tem Doran

The Angel of the North

Amy Angilley and Tamara Beach

Illustration:
Vicky Parker

 ey you!" William spun around to meet the venomous eyes of his arch-rival Dexter Davies. Dexter's tall, dark figure blurred as he leaned forward to take a forceful strike.

Reaching the comfort of his house, William bounced inside. "Hiya," he chirped, choking back the river of tears that flowed inside him. Some hours later, he collapsed into a deep sleep. Mumbling to himself, he muttered the words, "I wish I were somewhere else." With that, tiredness drifted over his misty brain.

All of a sudden, William eased his tense, battered body to a stand. He drew in a sharp, icy breath, before taking a step into a white, winter wilderness. The snow was white as a swan's elegant wings, and flurries sprinkled delicately across the outstretched plain.

Spinning frantically, a whirlwind of dazzling icicles cascaded into a figure, a human figure, with beautifully soft wings that blended into the pure carpet of snow.

"Who are you?" William stammered, his face struck with awe and wonder.

"I am the Angel of the North," explained the magical creature. "I am here to grant you one wish, and one wish only. Choose wisely, for you are the chosen one."

"I wish I wasn't bullied!" exclaimed William, and with that the angel rose up into the cool, calm air and disappeared in a puff of purple smoke.

All that remained was a jewel-encrusted box that glistened in the inky darkness. Cautiously he opened the box, revealing a waterfall of magic and mystery that exploded like ferocious fireworks.

Swish! A fierce gust of penetrating wind engulfed his body, sending him spiralling further and further away. Crash! William opened his topaz-tinted eyes to see his bedroom. He was sitting on his bed clasping a frozen icicle, whose bitter sharpness pierced his hands. In his ears were ringing the words: "Your wish is my command!"

Treasure

A wish is a treasure
So precious to me.
You can't hold it in your hands,
You couldn't throw it in the sea.

All you can do is keep it within
And then when you're ready,
Let it free.

It's something so special
That everyone has.

As long as you believe in it
It'll stay within your heart,
Until you finally believe
That it's time to part.

Bethany Penrose

Illustration:
Fatime Szaszi

A good friend in Cornwall

Katrina Bluett

I'm staying with my friend Charlotte in London, near the London Eye. Charlotte has blue, shiny eyes, short blond hair and a glamorous smile. Charlotte is a very nice girl but she gets spoilt.

She has lots of toys. She even has a television, a computer, an iPod, Nintendo and lots of other things. Charlotte seems happy, but deep down she's not happy with what she's got.

I could see sadness in her eyes. So I asked Charlotte if she wanted to come back to my house. Charlotte thought about it and in the end decided to come back with me. She reluctantly thought she would miss all her belongings in London, but she decided to come and stay with me in Cornwall.

Then, on Tuesday, we went out to walk in the countryside. The sun was shining, the birds were singing. We walked through the trees and eventually reached home. We were very hungry so I cooked us some dinner, then she asked if it was our farm. I whispered, "Yes, it is our farm. I was going to take you on a tour of the farm to see all the animals, if that's all right?" She answered, "That would be brilliant. Thanks." She enjoyed seeing all the animals.

Charlotte said, "I thought it was going to be really boring, but I realise now that you don't need lots of things to be happy, just a good friend." Then Charlotte whispered, "I wish I could stay here with you in Cornwall."

Illustration:
Natalie Belbin

38

Jack's wish

Grace Barnicoat

I sit and wait for Mum to
come home,
It's three in the morning
and I'm all alone.

I wish my Mum spent more time with me,
I wish my Mum didn't hurt me.

I'm only five, and I don't understand,
Instead of kisses I get slaps on my hands.

Dad comes home from the pub.
He never once has given me a hug.

"Jack!" he screams as he comes down the hall,
I run from my bedroom but come as he calls.

I wish he wasn't so angry with me,
I wish that he loved me.

He grabs a bottle and hits my head,
I scream and cry, I wish I could just go to bed.

My name is Jack and I am five,
In the morning I was no longer alive.

Illustration:
Jo Pascoe

39

Harry's rap

I'm called Harry,
I'm aged nine.
I'll be very happy
If you listen to my rhyme.
So don't just sit there having a snooze,
Come and help me spread the news.
I know the sky might be grey,
But if the ozone's destroyed
We'll all melt away.
People pollute the air by driving cars,
It makes smoke which travels very far.
Don't do too much driving
Because the fumes make me choke –
THAT'S NO JOKE.
Don't just sit there watching TV,
Turn it off – save electricity.
We get our oxygen from the trees,
Don't cut them down or else we won't be able to breathe.
Recycle your rubbish, don't throw it away,
Start recycling today.
Let's try not to pollute the sea,
It'll be no fun to play in for you and me.
If this planet has any worth
Come and help me save the earth!

Harrison Gilbert

Illusration:
Juan Moore

40

Tippy Toes

I wish one day I could have a pony,
I would call it Tippy Toes.
The colour would be chestnut brown
With a lovely pink nose.

I wish one day I could be a vet,
To help with the sick and old.
I'd always try my very best
With the pets I'd gently hold.

I wish one day I could be a unicorn,
With eyes of sparkly blue,
Spreading magic everywhere,
Making dreams come true.

Hollie Bennallick

Illustration:
Ellie Cryer

Every child

Class 5/6 Troon Primary School

W e wish every child could have their own home.
We wish every child could have a hot meal
And feel their taste buds tingle.
We wish every child had a warm, cosy bed to rest in
And a warm blanket to cover them at night.
We wish every child felt a calm breeze on their face.
We wish every child could feel the warmth and the
Freshness of a carpet underneath their feet.
We wish every child had a mum and a dad to keep them safe.
We wish every child could have the support
To keep them going through the sun and the rain.
We wish every child had a joyful family
That cared for them and loved them.
We wish every child had fun.
We wish every child could have their dream come true.
We wish everyone could have a life like ours.

Illustration:
Jasmine Foster

Comic book

Michael Stuart

I was reading a comic book,
I wished I was there.
But when I took a closer look
I was already there!
I looked around the corner
And saw a comic villain.
Then I looked behind me
And saw my best friend Dillon!
He told me to run,
I took his advice,
Then he blasted the villain
Once or maybe twice.
I asked him where he got his powers.
He said he didn't know,
But then I discovered
I had powers too!
I wished for this to happen,
Then my dream came true.
I wish, I wish, I wish…

Illustration
Ben Mounsey

Eight wishes

I f I had eight wishes, this is what they would be.
I wish there was no poverty.
I wish I was a doctor.
I wish I was a feather dancing on the breeze.
I wish there was more water for people in the world.
I wish children in India had money enough for school.
I wish the world was full of colour and no-one had a care.
I wish nobody suffered for other people's wrongs.
Finally, I wish people were happy with who and what they are.

Millie Jones

Illustration:
Levi Pinfold

Magic football boots

James Hosken

I wish for magic football boots.
I have magic feet and magic toes,
I hit the ball and in it goes!
I run on the wing,
I run real strong.
I shoot the ball short,
I shoot the ball long.
Tricks and skills are my trade,
My reactions are sharp as a well-made blade.
When I have a free kick, though I'm really quite small,
I've got the power to break the wall.
I run so fast it is quite frightening –
I'm like greased lightning.
I'm no David Beckham,
I'm no Ashley Cole,
But I am the boy
who can score the
goal!

Illustration:
Rachel Biddulph

Boyton's Licowish Allsorts

I wish that the world was made of toffee and sweets.
I wish that money grew on trees.
I wish that the poor countries had water, food and money.
I wish that everyone felt happy all the time.
I wish the sea tasted like lemonade.
I wish that sheep were made of candyfloss.
I wish that every day was like Christmas day.
I wish I could have a party every day of the year!
I wish that everyone would play nicely in the playground.
I wish that the world was nice and peaceful.
I hope these wishes will be granted!

Phoebe Fordham, Ocean Harrison, Lydia Mabbley, Gemma Mills, Rosie Sluggett and Oliver Sluggett

Illustration:
Lisa Zibamanzar Mofrad

Stories without horses

I wish I had a pony,
Not too fat and not too bony.
I wish that I were strong and fit,
Jumping on horses with all the kit.
I wish I owned my own stables,
And at school I knew all my tables.
I wish I could write stories without horses,
About swimming or gym or even cross-country courses!

Megan Wood

Illustration:
Lauren Nickless

Before it's out of use

Jacob Wilson

I wish for no terrorism,
I wish for no war,
I hope for empty prisons
So that crime is no more.

I wish for no cancer,
I wish for no colds,
I hope for more help
For when people grow old.

I wish for no poverty,
I wish for no hunger,
I hope for more food
To make the poor stronger.

I wish for global cooling,
I wish for greener fuels,
I hope the planet can be saved
Before it's out of use.

Illustration:
Nicole Lawson

Pony, cats and chocolate

I wish I could fly.
I wish I could travel the whole world.
I wish I had a horse or pony.
I wish my Mum was not allergic to cats so I could have one.
I wish I never got ill.
I wish I could have so much chocolate but not be sick,
And it was good for my teeth.
I wish I was never bad.

Lauren Flynn

Illutration:
Nick Mott

I could only wish

Lauren Newton

Illustration:
Vicky Jones

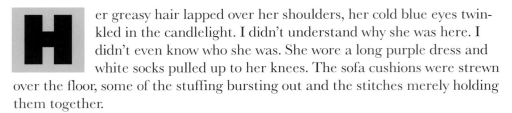

Her greasy hair lapped over her shoulders, her cold blue eyes twinkled in the candlelight. I didn't understand why she was here. I didn't even know who she was. She wore a long purple dress and white socks pulled up to her knees. The sofa cushions were strewn over the floor, some of the stuffing bursting out and the stitches merely holding them together.

The old woman suddenly turned her head towards where I was sitting, in the stair cupboard. Her nose was long and lumpy and looked unpleasantly out of shape. In fact, there was no other way to put it – she looked eerie.

Her head turned slightly so she was directly facing the cupboard. Was it that she knew she was being watched? By me?

"I wish I could be somewhere else right now!" was the thought going round in my head. My heart started to race, it was going faster and faster – I could feel my chest pounding with fear.

Her bony arm stretched towards the door handle. I could see her long, yellow nails and wrinkly fingers. My hands were trembling as I grabbed the door handle and threw myself out of the cupboard. I leapt up the stairs two at a time – three when I thought she was close.

"I wish, I wish…" I said to myself. "I wish I could be somewhere else right now!" Finally I reached the top of the stairs, sweating with fear. I held my eyes firmly closed with anticipation that any moment she would grab me.

I turned round with hesitation, only to find that I was alone. From that night on, I will always remember that eerie glimpse of her face, which will stay hidden at the back of my mind forever. But the question I keep asking myself is, will she be back? I can only wish that she never returns!

Perfect Persian

Alexandra Strike

I wish I had a cat,
A perfect, Persian pretty kitty.
Purring on my lap,
Just about to have a nap,
Pawing slowly to her bowl,
Exactly like she knows it all.
She would be as soft as silk,
And would be as white as milk.
The gorgeous girl would dance and twirl,
A dancer born to be.
And when that Persian cat came by,
I'd keep it all for me.

Illustration:
Genna Byrne

Too late for wishes

Dominique Sansom

Jack woke up. His hair, still thick but now white, stood on end as he hobbled to the window and stared at the bleached wilderness below.

The damage beneath could never be repaired. Jack's garden looked like a rubbish tip. Dead trees stood like old soldiers in the corners of the garden. Tin cans and broken glass bottles lay scattered amongst the golden leaves on the lawn; snapped branches lay outside the front gate.

Every night without fail, a group of men came with a bin and tipped most of its contents onto his lawn. Why they did this, Jack didn't know, but he could guess – there was nowhere else to put it. All the landfill sites had been filled up because people had not recycled their rubbish. All their waste had to go somewhere, so where did it go? On the streets and on people's lawns. Jack felt too old to challenge these men.

As Jack stared across the landscape a whisper slipped out from between his lips.

"I wish we had done something. I wish we had listened. I wish we had recycled our waste."

But then he heard his wife calling him for breakfast from downstairs and he sighed. Painfully, old Jack hobbled down the stairs to see her.

Illustration:
Sarah Croker

53

Joyful creatures

Nicola Smith

I wish I was a butterfly,
Flying round the garden,
Showing off my scarlet wings
With their dark ebony patterns.

I wish I was a dolphin,
Darting through the ocean,
Calling out to other dolphins
And making friends with divers.

I wish I was a tiger,
Running through the jungle,
Hiding in the bushes
And climbing up trees.

I wish I was a wild horse,
Galloping across the moors,
Bucking and neighing
And eating grass.

I wish I was a rabbit,
Hopping though the fields,
Nibbling the long green grass
And tunnelling under the ground.

Illustration:
Kasia Dudziuk

Tigers

Terrible things happen to tigers.
Isolated and cut off from family,
Grounded and caged, the tiger is defeated.
Expecting rewards the poachers stand proud.
Roaring aloud the tiger makes his last stand.
Surely hunting should be banned.

Victoria Sharpe

Illustration:
Scarlet A. Gutteridge

Isabel the pop star

Emily Spargo

Illustration:
Kathrine Kristiansen

wish I'd never been born. I absolutely hate it here!"
Isabel screamed down the phone to her trusty friend Jessie.
"I wish I was like you. You're rich and popular and
I'm just poor and lonely."

"No you're not – you're my friend," said Jessie softly.

"Thanks Jess."

"Well I've got to go – my Mum is going to take me out shopping," said Jessie before hanging up.

What was there to do? Jessie had gone, Mum and Dad had gone away to a friend's party and Jake, Daniel, Amy and Holly had gone out with friends. Just Isabel on her own in this boring, damp place.

"I absolutely hate it. Mum and Dad never take notice of me and the others don't care at all!"

Then Isabel had a great idea. She would run away! As nobody cared, she could run away to be a famous pop star!

Ding-dong! It was Mum and Dad. Isabel scooped up her purse and everything she needed and stuffed it in her small bag.

"Isabel, are you there?" shouted her mum.

Isabel unlocked the door and shouted: "It's open!" Then she made a run for the back door as Mum and Dad came stomping in. She tried to close the back door softly but she had to do it quickly, as mum was practically in the room as Isabel left. BANG! went the door as she zoomed out and through the garden.

Isabel soon found a nice place to sing for money, down at the bay, and after a few years she got used to it. One day she was singing when a strange man came up to her and said: "You're the next big thing."

"You think so?"

"Yes. Did you hear what you just sang? Sing it again!"

"OK… *It's a new life, got to hear what your heart is saying. It's a new life, got to get used to living this way. It's a new life, got to hear what people are saying. So let's keep it this way.*"

"Stop!"

"Why?"

"Why? Because I was about to cry, that's why. And I want you to make a record at the Royal Studio in London!"

A few months later, Isabel thought to herself, "Why did I leave Mum and Dad?" So one night she got some tickets for her next show and posted them to her family.

On the night she was singing beautifully when she suddenly said: "Stop the music!"

It was her family – Mum and Dad, Jake, Amy, Daniel and Holly! Isabel ran as fast as she could through the crowd to be with them.

Isabel gave up singing to live with her family.

57

Perfect world

Grace Holland

I wish I lived in a perfect world,
Where there were no poachers, wars,
Fighting or bullies.
But it takes more than a wish
For that to come true.

I wish I lived in a perfect world,
Where there was no poverty,
Famine or pollution.
But it takes more than a wish
For that to come true.

I wish I lived in a perfect world,
Where there were no murderers,
Suicide bombers or terrorists.
But it takes more than a wish
For that to come true.

I wish I lived in a perfect world,
Where people were kind, generous,
Loving and forgiving.
But it takes more than a wish
For that to come true.

But if we all try we just might succeed,
Only if we try.

Illustration:
Solveig Wiig

Escape into Narnia

After the Art Club, I walk home alone,
Scared of the bullies I have to pass by.
I wish I could hide or escape from their reach,
Dissolve from their sight or… I wish I could fly!

I've landed in Narnia, there's a lamp-post in sight,
Fir trees and fauns, Susan's bow, Centaur's spear.
Aslan roars from the castle called Caer Paravel,
King Peter says, "Welcome. You've nothing to fear."

Charlotte Moyle

Illustration:
Julie Parker

Wishes for Africa

I wish for no drought so that crops can be eaten.
I wish for Africa to have clean water, so diseases can be beaten.
I wish for Africa to have more clever medical staff.
I wish for all African children to stop crying and start to laugh.
I wish that Africa's fruit will grow healthy and ready to pick.
I wish that the rude rich countries would give more to the poor and sick.
I wish that the crops would grow healthy in Africa,
Like fresh summer fruit in the midday sun.
I wish that African children had comfy clothes, games and lots of fun.

Hannah Leggatt

Illustration:
Ellen Janman

Just me

Jordan Vincent

 wish I was an astronaut,
Floating in space.
I wish I was a clown
With a funny face.

I wish I was a lizard-keeper
Scaring all my friends.
I wish I was a racing driver
Steering round the bends.

I wish I was a magician
Doing lots of magic shows.
Or flying in an aeroplane –
Where could I go?

One day I'll be grown up
I wonder what I'll be?
I'm happy at the moment
To just be ME!

Illustration:
Kosei Kawakubo

Ben

This is a story about a child. His name was Ben and he lived in a big house with a man called Samuel Rich. Ben did not have any parents, or family for that matter, and he was ill-treated and used as a slave. He had to cook, clean and shop. If he was late, he got hurt.

One day someone knocked on the door.

"Get it Ben", ordered Samuel Rich.

Ben opened the door. It was a big man called Pat. Pat had been watching the house and had reported Samuel Rich to the NSPCC.

In the end Ben got a nice home with a family who loved him.

I wish that every child who is ill-treated could be helped.

Joshua Tully

Illustration:
David Bain

No pollution

I wish for no pollution,
It chokes our lovely world.
I wish for no landfill sites,
They scab the whole landscape.
I wish for no wasted material,
It just squanders away our plastic, paper and glass.
I wish there were electric cars,
All the fumes do is suffocate the atmosphere.
I wish people never threw litter on the streets,
All they do is ruin our wonderful world.

Rhys Hewitt

Illustration:
Fiona Gowen

Sam the footballer

Sam was happiest playing football. He thought, talked and dreamt football. His greatest wish was to become a professional football player. However, he always seemed to be in the wrong place at the wrong time. His mother was constantly saying, "You'll never be a professional football player!"

One Sunday he went along – as he always did without fail – to his local club, the Cobras, to train for the Sunday League match. But during training everything that could go wrong went wrong. First, he missed a really easy pass. Later, he tripped over his own shoelaces. To cap it all, he took an open shot at the goal, which just happened to be his own net!

After training the coach made the selection for the match. Sam was devastated to be named sub. All he could think about were his mother's words.

Sam Mills

When the day arrived, Sam arrived at the ground with a heavy heart. He saw all his team-mates crowding around the coach. It turned out that Jason, their centre forward, had fallen off his bike and broken his leg. Seeing Sam, the coach turned to him and said, "You'll have to play this morning. Just focus on the ball and make sure your laces are done up tight."

During the first half, Sam managed to score a fantastic goal, but unfortunately against his own team. As the goalie dived for the ball, he smashed into the goalpost, knocking himself out!

At half time the coach decided that Sam would cause least damage if he were goalkeeper. And all of a sudden Sam's luck seemed to change. He dived. He ducked. He jumped fearlessly! Most importantly, he saved ball after ball. The final score was 5-1 to the Cobras.

Sam was named man of the match. Mum was so proud of him. She hugged him saying, "You star! Maybe you will be a professional football player after all!" Will Sam's wish come true?

Illustration:
Tone Schmidt

Clean and calm as a dove

We wish that tigers could run free with their tails curled.
We wish the world was as beautiful as it once was.
We wish the antelopes still leaped in safety.
We wish that there was no such thing as war
And that people didn't have to go to fight.
We wish that there was no such thing as poverty.
We wish the world was as clean and calm as a dove.

Zoe Scholes & Poppy Brydon

Illustration
Silje Hellesen

A spoiled child

Matthew was selfish. He didn't ever send thank-you notes, even at Christmas. On top of this, his parents were idiots who gave him anything he wanted. The result was a spoiled and ungrateful child.

One day, Matthew demanded a holiday to Africa. "OK son, whatever you say," said his Dad. The next week it was all booked, and the week after that they were on the plane.

When they landed in Africa they got into a taxi. Suddenly the taxi stopped and Franco, the driver, got out. "Doesn't look good," said Matthew's Dad, pointing to the smoking bonnet. They had stopped next to a battered old shanty town.

Alice Hunter

"Oh, great!" said Matthew sarcastically. "I'm stuck next to a rubbish dump!"

"Your boy looks ill," said the taxi driver. "Oh no!" said Matthew's parents, "Is it serious?"

'Not so much serious as contagious," said Franco. "Leave him with me tonight – you can come and get him tomorrow, when he is cured."

"Okay," said his parents, "We'll pick him up tomorrow." Those were their last words before they hopped onto an old, battered bicycle and wobbled away into the darkness.

"Is this a rubbish yard?" asked Matthew pointing at the shanty town. "A rubbish yard!" said Franco, sounding outraged. "This is our home. Come on, let's go in."

Matthew moaned all the way up to the old gate that was the entrance to that depressing place. As soon as Matthew stepped through the gates he stopped in shock. "Oh my God!" he exclaimed.

Illustration:
Robin Boyden

"Not all people are as lucky as you," said Franco.

66

"Anyway, you look tired. Come with me and I will ask for a bed for you to sleep in tonight."

"OK," said Matthew shakily. He was still in shock from seeing a little girl drinking water as clear as mud.

That night he lay in a bed of newspaper on the floor of an old wooden shack. He was hungry, as he had only had a handful of rice for his supper, which was hardly anything compared to his usual two helpings of spaghetti.

Then he heard voices speaking. He listened closely and this is what he heard.

"I wish we had clean water," said one child. "I wish we had enough food to go round," said another. But the last wish was the one that Matthew felt most guilty about.

"I wish that I had one toy," said the last child sadly. That was when Matthew thought of all the toys at home that he never played with.

The next morning, Matthew's parents came to pick him up. "Are you feeling better now?" they asked. "Yes," said Matthew. "Never better."

But do you know what Matthew wished for that night? No, it wasn't a Playstation 2.

"I wish," said Matthew, "that everyone was a lucky as me." And guess what? Matthew NEVER demanded anything again.

Eye on
the ball

Shooting and passing, headering and saving,
These are the skills, and I practise them all.
I'll get to Old Trafford and play for United
If only I keep my eye on the ball!

Arms flapping, feet running, heart beating so fast,
I'm ready for take-off, my head in the sky.
At the edge of the cliff I look down and I know
I'm a boy not a bird, and I never can fly.

Paul Richards

Illustration:
James Cottell

Spain

I wish I could be on holiday all the time.
I would go to the park and climb and climb.

I wish I could swim for miles in the calm blue sea.
Just Mum, Dad, Rosie and me.

I wish I could eat lots of chocolate ice cream.
Lie on my favourite beach towel and have a beautiful dream.

I wish I could stay up late with Mum and Dad.
I would beat them at hangman and Dad would be mad.

I wish I could go to Spain on holiday again!

Harriet Bolton

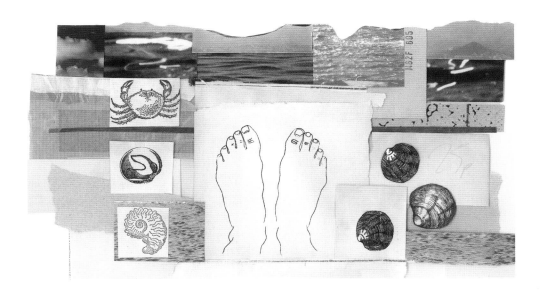

Illustration:
Viola Rank-Broadly

A country dream

Henry Giles

 dreamed a dream the other night that I was the kennel man looking after the foxhounds. I dreamed that the farmers could go out shooting without people protesting, and that the hunt could go out freely without breaking the law.

I dreamed that people could go out walking, not worrying about whose land they were on, that people would all hold hands and get on with each other.

I dreamed that the fields and woods were blooming with wildlife; that lambs played on the downs and birds sang overhead, and that children played by the streams when the adults went out hunting.

I dreamed of local men and children helping all the farmers bring in the hay, with the kids playing with the dogs or making dens.

I dreamed that there were no televisions or computers, but families playing cards and board games to pass the time on rainy days, with all the animals safely in their beds.

I dreamed a dream the other night, lying down in bed – what a picture-perfect world! I wish our world was like it.

Illustration:
Caroline Metcalfe

Seventy-foot trailer

I wish I had a dragon and could fly over the mountain tops.
I wish I could stop world poverty and give everyone enough food to sink a battleship.
I wish I had a 70-foot trailer so me and my family could live in it.
I wish I could be the next Elvis Presley.
I wish I could stop ageing at 20 years old.
I wish I could go back in time.
I wish I had a stretch limo with twenty doors on each side.

Ollie Bowers

Illustration:
Kathrine Kristiansen

Friend to friend

Lara Reutsch

I wish I could be Kelly Holmes,
Running so fast it would rattle my bones.

I wish all the wars would end,
So everybody could stand friend to friend.

I wish I could eat chocolate for tea,
Not for anyone else, just for me!

I wish I could fly into space,
Jump into a rocket, leaving without a trace.

I wish everybody could get on,
Then the world would never go wrong.

Illustration:
Louise Bartlett

Fairy Daffodil

Olive Parker

ne warm Sunday I was sitting in the garden when suddenly I heard a voice.

"Hello! Is anyone there?"

I turned round. "Who's that talking?" I asked curiously.

"Fairy Daffodil," the voice replied, and then I noticed her. She was a lovely fairy, all dressed in yellow and about as big as my rubber. She smiled at me.

"Do you want a wish?" she asked.

"Oh yes!" I said happily. I wished that I could shrink and that when I wanted I could grow again.

The fairy's house was a daffodil, and I peeped inside. But as I was looking around, I heard a noise – it was a bumblebee! We were both frightened – what would a bumblebee look like if we were this size? I ran and hid, but Fairy Daffodil was too late. She screamed!

I grabbed some wings and flew home, quickly found a pin, and then flew back to the fairy as fast as I could and pricked the bee. "Hurray!" shouted Fairy Daffodil.

I went out of the daffodil and never went inside it again. But I do still see the fairy fluttering around the garden sometimes.

Illustration:
Lisa Ford

73

Strawberry milkshake

I wish I could run across the fields on a summer's day
And ask the cows if they could make some milk.
Then I would squeeze some strawberries
To make some strawberry milkshake, and sit on a beach.
After that, I'd go home and have a nice long sleep.

Phoebe Allingham

Illustration:
Silje Hellesen

Dazzly dolphin, slimy elephant

May Robson

If I could, I'd like to splash and leap in the deep blue sea.
I would squeal my squeally sound, to catch food.
I'd love to dance with mermaids,
Glide through the watery waves.
I would play tricks, swim really fast.
I wish I was a dazzly dolphin.

If I could, I would like to charge around in the jungle,
I would show my huge body to other animals,
Shoot water right up in the air,
Drink from the waterhole,
Make myself fall, and straight
I would crush down trees!
Splash in the lake and get soaking,
Stand in a line and make my ginormous booming sound.
I wish I was a slippery, slimy elephant.

Illustration:
Kine Solberg

75

Differences

I wish I wasn't different,
I would like to be the same,
As people always stare at me
And call me hurtful names.

I wish I wasn't big,
I would like to be the same.
Others stay away from me,
It's all because of my shape.

I wish I wasn't short,
I would like to be the same.
People always laugh at me
And won't let me join their games.

I wish I had some friends
To stand there by my side,
And even if I'm different,
I'm sure they wouldn't mind.

Tamara Stidwell

Illustration:
Ben Mounsley

The ideal mouse

Jimmy Williams

 wish I had a mouse.
A mouse that can talk,
A mouse that can walk on its
Own two feet!
One that is very brainy,
Fun to play with
When the day is rainy!
Not too hard to look after.
When I'm sad I want him to
Make me fall over with laughter
By doing tricks,
Including flips.
That's the ideal mouse I wish.

Illustration:
Nick Mott

Dreams that come true every night

Katie Morton

Illustration:
Kasia Dudziak

I wish I had a pony
To carry me away,
Over the snowy mountains
To places far away.

She'd take me far across the sea,
Across the deserts too,
To see the sort of animals
That you can see in a zoo.

I wish I was invisible
So no would see me
Raiding the kitchen cupboards,
Not eating up all my tea.

I could hide from my sister
When she wants to play,
And have my own space
In my bedroom to play.

But I don't need to wish
For my dreams like some people do.
In my snug bed at night
All these things come true.

All the above

Eleanor Toms

 wish the world could be a beautiful place,
No fighting, no cruelty, no hatred.
For people to live in unity,
Each given their own personal space.

I wish that everyone had plenty to eat,
No starving, no poverty, no illnesses.
And no-one would be homeless,
But have clothes on their bodies and shoes on their feet.

I wish the world could be beautiful,
Bright colours, pretty flowers and sunny days.
No pollution, no darkness, no emptiness,
But fresh water, clean air and pure ways.

I wish that everyone could enjoy what I have to love,
My family, my friends and my cosy home.
But it isn't a perfect world, I know,
And I'm grateful for all the above.

Illustration:
Katy Wright

Baby brother

I had a little wish
For a little baby brother.
I got my baby wish,
But now he is a bother!

Stealing all my things
And pulling at my hair.
But inside I love him really,
With his curly, curly hair!

Catherine Buckland

Illustration:
Carys Williams

Shiny fish

I wish that I could be a fish
With a very shiny body,
And go on adventures far and wide,
And find hidden treasures in the sand.
As I go by, I say "Hi!"
I smile at the whales,
And wink at the fish with the stripy pink tails.

Ella Wall

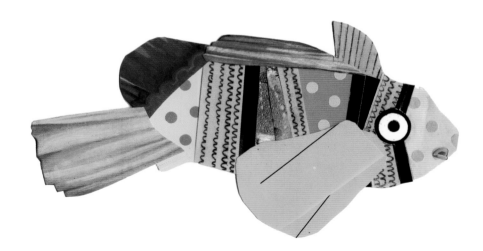

Illustration:
Zoe Bryant

82

You

Some people wish they were heroes,
Some people wish they were rich,
Some people wish they could fly up high,
And some people wish they were big.
But all I really wish for is you.

Some people wish they looked younger,
Some people wish not to die,
Some people wish they could be wizards,
And some people that they were fish.
But if I had one wish I think it would be this:
I wish I could be with you.

Some people wish they were giants,
Some people wish they were stars,
Some people wish they could touch the sky,
And some people wish for world peace.
But all that I really want
And all that I really wish for is you.

Jacob Dyer

Illustration:
Vicki Parker

83

People working together

Class 4
Goonhavern Primary School

We all wish that our environment was always clean.
No pollution, no poisonous gases,
No plastic littering our countryside.
No roadkill lying beside roads
Through thoughtless speeding cars.

We all wish that people would stop cutting down trees,
Endangering animals lives,
Ruining the habitats of animals and humans,
Taking away the natural cover,
Wrecking the beauty of their habitat.

We all have dreams
Of flowers rising,
Animals growing,
Nature all around us flourishing.

People working together
To protect our environment.
Helping us to farm our land,
Sharing our food,
Curing diseases.
To live happily,
Helping the poor of this world,
Making poverty history.

Illustration:
Vicky Jones

Everything free

I wish that there were no underage smokers.
I wish that dogs didn't wear chokers.
I wish that no-one ever died.
I wish that people didn't cry.
I wish that nobody was mean.
I wish that people ate their greens.
I wish that people were safe at sea.
I wish that everything was free!

Hannah Miles

Illustration:
Amy Riches

Seasons

**Ester Curry, Faith Ogilvie and
Lowenna Mentis**

I wish I could sit on the river bank,
The river charging past like a military tank.
The willow trees' branches swish and sway,
The sun beaming down in the middle of May.
Row down the river between the reeds...
This simple life contains all your needs.
The sheep in the field like little white clouds,
Listening to a waterfall gushing so loud.

I wish I could stand, my welly boots so big,
The rain dropping down over every small twig.
Brown mud oozes into the water,
Pull up your skirt to make it shorter!
Ripples grow, building out from the centre,
With every jump as my feet re-enter.
Grey clouds building overhead,
The earth turning a dull shade of red.

I wish I could stand with the leaves at my feet,
Look up at the sky where all the trees meet.
The dying leaves drift languidly to the ground,
The floor turning into a golden mound.
The path a carpet of red and yellow,
Birds twitter their farewell ever so mellow.
The ripened berries turn a soft sort of brown,
Weighing the long spiky brambles down.

But here I am, stuck in my room,
My dull face portraying nothing but gloom.

Illustration:
Rachel Boulton

Edible world

I wish the trees were made of broccoli.
I wish the sea was made of Vimto.
I wish the mud was made of melted chocolate.
I wish the grass was made of candy sticks.
I wish the clouds were made of candy floss.
I wish the leaves were made of lettuce.
I wish my bed was made of gold.
I wish I had a pet dragon.
I wish my hamster didn't die.
I wish bushes were made of brussel sprouts.

Ben Clark

Illustration:
Scarlet A. Gutteridge

Wise wishes on the beach

Lily Hayes

But I want to go to the beach," demanded Isabelle.

"But I really think..." said her Mum, before she was interrupted by Isabelle's nagging.

"NO!" Isabelle shouted.

Eventually Isabelle got her own way. They parked the car near Pebble Beach and walked along the sand until they found a quiet, shaded spot at the far end. Isabelle's Mum laid down a mat for them to sit on.

Where's my swimming costume?" begged Isabelle. Her mother passed her a frilly pink costume. Isabelle struggled as she clambered into it. As quick as a blink, she skipped off merrily down the shore, carrying her bucket and spade with her. When she got down to the sea she spotted an animal that was stuck between two rocks. It had a long, shimmering tail that glinted in the afternoon sun, and beautiful long scarlet hair. Isabelle pulled it up above the water.

"Thank you," whispered the creature, who had a sort of French accent. "Now you have rescued me I will give you three wishes."

"I wish... " said Isabelle quickly.

"No," said the mermaid (Isabelle had realised what she was now). "Use your wishes wisely – remember your father."

How do you know about him?" asked Isabelle.

"Ah, I know everything!" whispered the mermaid.

"Right, I wish my Dad would come home safely," said Isabelle.

Illustration:
Clare Elsom

88

"One," whispered the mermaid.

"I wish that me and my mum could get on."

"Two," whispered the mermaid. "Anything else?"

"No," said Isabelle.

"But you've got one last wish left."

"I know," replied Isabelle.

"OK," the mermaid said. "I'll just go now."

"Wait!" Isabelle shouted after her. "I do have one more wish."

"And what's that?" whispered the mermaid.

"I wish I had some friends."

"One, two, three!" the mermaid shouted, and suddenly she just vanished.

"Mum... Mum!" Isabelle shouted as she ran up the sand. "I just met a mermaid!"

"And I just met an octopus," said her Mum sarcastically.

The National Society for the Prevention of Cruelty to Children (NSPCC) is the UK's leading charity specialising in child protection and the prevention of cruelty to children. Its vision is of a society where all children are loved, valued and able to fulfil their potential.

Eighty-three per cent of the work the NSPCC does is made possible by voluntary donations. By buying this book you are helping to end cruelty to children. FULL STOP. We'd like to thank you for caring.

Did you know …?

The NSPCC has been helping and protecting children, and campaigning on their behalf, since 1884. These days, its work includes:

Around 180 community-based teams and projects delivering services throughout England, Wales, the Channel Islands and Northern Ireland

A free, 24-hour Child Protection Helpline (0808 800 5000) for anyone who has concerns about the welfare of a child

Public education campaigns to increase understanding about child abuse and provide advice and support on positive parenting and child protection

Parliamentary campaigning aimed at putting children's issues at the top of the political agenda

Child protection training and advice for organisations involved in the care, protection and education of children, for example sports bodies

Research into the nature and effects of child abuse

Information on child protection and related topics for the general public, professionals and the media

With your support, the NSPCC can continue to make a real difference to children in your local community. For more information on how you can help the NSPCC as a volunteer or supporter, please visit www.nspcc.org.uk or call the Appeals Team on 01823 346346.

Illustration
Silje Hellesen

Participating Schools

Altarnun Community Primary School

Archbishop Benson C of E Primary School, Truro

Bishop Bronescombe C of E VA School, St Austell

Boyton Community Primary School

Calstock Community Primary School

Charlestown Primary School

Constantine Primary School

Cubert School

Cury C of E Primary School

Coverack Community Primary School

Germoe Community Primary School

Goonhavern Primary School

Kea Community Primary School

Kennall Vale School, Ponsanooth

King Charles Primary School, Falmouth

Landewednack Community Primary School

Liskeard Junior School

Luxulyan School

Mabe Community Primary School

Mithian School

Newlyn School

Probus Community Primary School

Roselyon School, Par

St Breock Primary School, Wadebridge

St Buryan Primary School

St Martin-in-Meneage Community Primary School

St Mary's Catholic Primary School, Falmouth

St Mark's C of E Primary School, Morwenstow

St Nicolas' C of E VA School, Downderry

St Wenn School, Bodmin

Tintagel Primary School

Troon Community Primary School

Tywardreath School

Whitstone Community Primary School

SPONSORS

WE WISH TO THANK

The We Wish project could not have happened without the generous help of many individuals and organisations. Special thanks are due to:

Kelsall Steele, whose staff raised more than £6,000 towards production costs, and also helped with financial planning and marketing for the project; **Hine Downing Solicitors**, who also contributed generously to the book's production costs; **The Paul Smales Trust**, who sponsored the writing competition; **Louise Cooper** and **Karen King**, who judged the competition; **Thandie Newton**, who made time in a busy schedule to write a foreword; **Ian Grant**, who gave invaluable publishing advice at every stage of the project; **Peter Bennett**, who designed the book so beautifully; **Stuart Odgers**, who helped organise the book's production; **Howard Smith Papers** who subsidised the paper on which the book is printed; **Tormark Press**, who helped distribute the book; **Sandra Myers** of the NSPCC's West Cornwall branch; all the **students and staff at University College Falmouth** who gave so unstintingly of their time and creativity – especially **Tom Scott** of the MA Professional Writing course, who co-ordinated the project.

And last – but by no means least – we'd like to thank all the **brilliant children and their teachers** whose talents and imagination have made We Wish such a special book.

THESE WISHES

MAY COME TRUE